VISIONS

for Jeremy Dale

CLARINET in B♭

I

PAUL HARRIS

Allegro ma non troppo, poco maestoso (♩ = 96)

AB 2363

for Sam Edenborough

Lento e molto espressivo (♩=48)   IV

for Alan Jones

V

Allegro vigoroso (♩ = 132)

Paul Harris

Visions

Five moderately difficult
pieces for clarinet and piano

The Associated Board of
the Royal Schools of Music

VISIONS

for Jeremy Dale

I

PAUL HARRIS

Allegro ma non troppo, poco maestoso (♩ = 96)

AB 2363

for Katy Burke

II

Adagio, molto cantabile ($\quarternote$ = 60)

for Nicholas Smith

III

for Sam Edenborough

IV

9

AB 2363

for Alan Jones

V